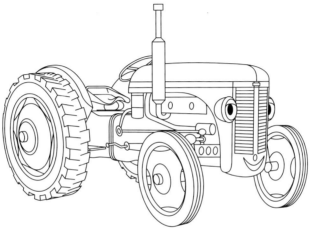

FERGUS' BONFIRE NIGHT

It was a cold and bright Autumn day. Everything was crisp with frost and glittering in the sunshine.

Farmer Pete and Steve the Handyman had been busy with the tractors all morning.

Fergus the Tractor and his friend Berty the Thirty were helping them collect wood from around the farm.

As they gathered the wood they took it to a nearby field. There with the help of Young Timmy, Steve the Handyman stacked the wood in a big pile.

The stack of wood was getting bigger and bigger, it was beginning to look like an upside down ice cream cone.

"I really don't know why Farmer Pete is doing this," said Fergus to Berty.

"Perhaps Farmer Pete is just tidying up," replied Berty who wasn't sure either.

"Farmer Pete normally collects the wood to use on the fires in the farmhouse," said Fergus. "I wonder why he is piling it up here?"

"We will have to wait and see," replied Berty. "I am sure Farmer Pete has a good reason."

Later in the day, when it was beginning to get dark, Farmer Pete came back to the barn with Young Timmy.

They started up Fergus and Berty and drove them to the nearby field, where all of the villagers and their children were waiting for Farmer Pete.

Some of the villagers were sitting on logs, some were talking to friends and some of the children were playing games.

Farmer Pete stopped Fergus and asked the villagers to make sure that the children were at a safe distance away from the wood pile.

When he was sure that everyone was safe and having checked the wood pile for hedgehogs, Farmer Pete lit a small fire at the base.

Soon all of the wood pile was alight. It was the biggest bonfire the village had ever seen. It lit up the field, it lit up the sky and it lit up everyones faces.

With Fergus and Berty parked far enough away from the fire, Farmer Pete opened a big box that had been placed on the trailer.

One by one he took out some strange tubes and smaller boxes and placed them on the ground.

He closed the lid of the big box and after checking that everyone was safe, he carefully lit some of the tubes.

As Farmer Pete lit the tubes, they started to smoke. Suddenly sparks and glitter poured from the tops.

At first Fergus and Berty were surprised and a little scared. They had never seen fireworks before.

All of the fireworks were different, some whooshed and whistled, some crackled and banged. All of them burst out with bright colourful sparks of glitter.

Soon they knew there was nothing to be scared of and started to enjoy the fireworks.

There were sparklers that sizzled and rockets that whistled and banged, showering the sky with all kinds of bright sparkling colours.

Everyone in the village clapped and cheered as they enjoyed the bonfire and the fireworks display.

They were also enjoying the hot food and drinks that Farmer Pete's wife Ann had brought along.

There were pies and pasties, hot dog sausages and jacket potatoes cooked in the bottom of the bonfire, with sticky chocolate cake and toffee apples to finish.

All the villagers and their children were enjoying the bonfire night. Farmer Pete was having a great time lighting the fireworks and watching them whizz off into the night sky.

The firework display ended and the night drew to a close.
As everyone began to leave, the vicar said thank you to Farmer Pete
and Ann for a really enjoyable evening.

He told Farmer Pete that the whole village had a wonderful time
watching the bonfire and the firework display.

Once everyone had gone, Farmer Pete, his wife and Young Timmy
made their way back to the farm with
Fergus and Berty.

As Fergus and Berty were put back in the barn, Farmer Pete thanked them for their help. "Without you we could not have built such a big bonfire," said Farmer Pete. "Sleep well, you both deserve it."

As Farmer Pete closed the doors Fergus and Berty decided to go straight to sleep. There would be lots of time tomorrow to talk about the wonderful bonfire and fireworks.

With that they closed their eyes and went
to sleep under their blankets.

FERGUS' STORY   MR COOMBS THE GAMEKEEPER   GEOF
THE MECHANIC   FERGUS GETS A NEW FRIEND   NEVILL
GETS HIS NAME   NEVILLE AND THE HOT AIR BALLOO
FERGUS' BONFIRE NIGHT   FERGUS AT THE BARN FIR
FERGUS AND BERTY CLEAR THE SNOW   FERGUS' CHRISTMA
SPECIAL   THE SPRING TIME SURPRISE   FERGUS AND TH
NEW BUILDING   FERGUS' HALLOWEEN   FERGUS AND TH
STEAM UP   FERGUS AND BERTY GO POTATO PLANTIN
FERGUS AND THE BEAVER SCOUTS   THE WEDDING DA
FERGUS AND THE FLOOD   FERGUS AT THE CIRCUS   FERGU
AND THE HEATWAVE   FERGUS AT THE CARNIVAL   FERGU
AT THE PLOUGHING MATCH   FERGUS AND THE FALLEN TRE
FERGUS' STORY   MR COOMBS THE GAMEKEEPER   GEOF
THE MECHANIC   FERGUS GETS A NEW FRIEND   NEVILL
GETS HIS NAME   NEVILLE AND THE HOT AIR BALLOO
FERGUS' BONFIRE NIGHT   FERGUS AT THE BARN FIR
FERGUS AND BERTY CLEAR THE SNOW   FERGUS' CHRISTMA